Albus Dumbledore
Headmaster of Hogwarts School of Witchcraft and Wizardry. He sports a very long beard – the attribute of the wisest wizards!

Rubeus Hagrid
The gamekeeper and Care of Magical Creatures teacher at Hogwarts. He wouldn't hurt a fly ... unless it was a Death Eater.

Hermione Granger
Harry and Ron's best friend. Her parents are Muggles, but she has a unique flair for magic.

Ron Weasley
Harry's loyal friend, famous for his sense of humour and loyalty.

Harry Potter
The boy who lived. The chosen one. The ... oh, never mind. Everybody knows him!

Lord Voldemort
Leader of the Death Eaters and Harry Potter's worst enemy. He's a gifted wizard who made the wizarding world tremble.

Severus Snape
Potions Master with a complex history. He liked Harry, then he didn't like him, then he saved his life, then ... it's complicated.

Build the Snape minifigure – maybe it'll help you spot the professor quicker. Then turn the page and let the search and find fun begin!

DIAGON ALLEY

Barty Crouch Jr.

Mme. Hooch

Arthur Weasley

Prof. Snape

Prof. Lupin

Filch

Harry

Hermione

Draco Malfoy

Ron

THE GREAT HALL

Hermione

Filch

Prof. Snape

Ron

Cho

Fred

Dean

Prof. Flitwick

Neville

MOVING STAIRCASES

Hagrid

Prof. McGonagall

Malfoy

Prof. Snape

Prof. Lockhart

Prof. Trelawney

Hermione

Dobby

Neville

CORNISH PIXIES

Prof. Snape

Harry

Hermione

Filch

Prof. Lockhart

Ron

Goyle

Neville

Dean

PLATFORM 9¾

Arthur Weasley

Barty Crouch Jr.

Prof. McGonagall

Narcissa Malfoy

Sirius Black

Tonks

Prof. Snape

Ron

Molly Weasley

Trolley Lady

Kingsley Shacklebolt

Prof. Lupin

QUIDDITCH

Prof. Trelawney

Filch

Prof. Dumbledore

Goblin

Dobby

Sirius Black

Prof. Snape

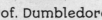

Cho

Dean

Ron

FIREWORKS

"Mad-Eye" Moody

Hermione

Cho

Luna

Prof. Sprout

Malfoy

Mme. Hooch

Prof. Snape

Bellatrix Lestrange

10 10 10 10

MINISTRY OF MAGIC

Peter Pettigrew

Prof. Lupin

Goyle

Prof. Snape

Trolley Lady

Molly Weasley

Hagrid

Kingsley Shacklebolt

Oliver

Prof. Sprout

WEASLEYS' WIZARD WHEEZES

Molly Weasley

Harry

Filch

Prof. Lupin

Malfoy

Hermione

Oliver

Prof. Snape

Prof. McGonagall

Prof. Slughorn

Prof. Flitwick

Sirius Black

GRINGOTTS WIZARDING BANK

Prof. McGonagall   Tonks   Prof. Snape   Filch   Dobby   Voldemort   Fred   Trolley Ladg   Harry

BATTLE OF HOGWARTS

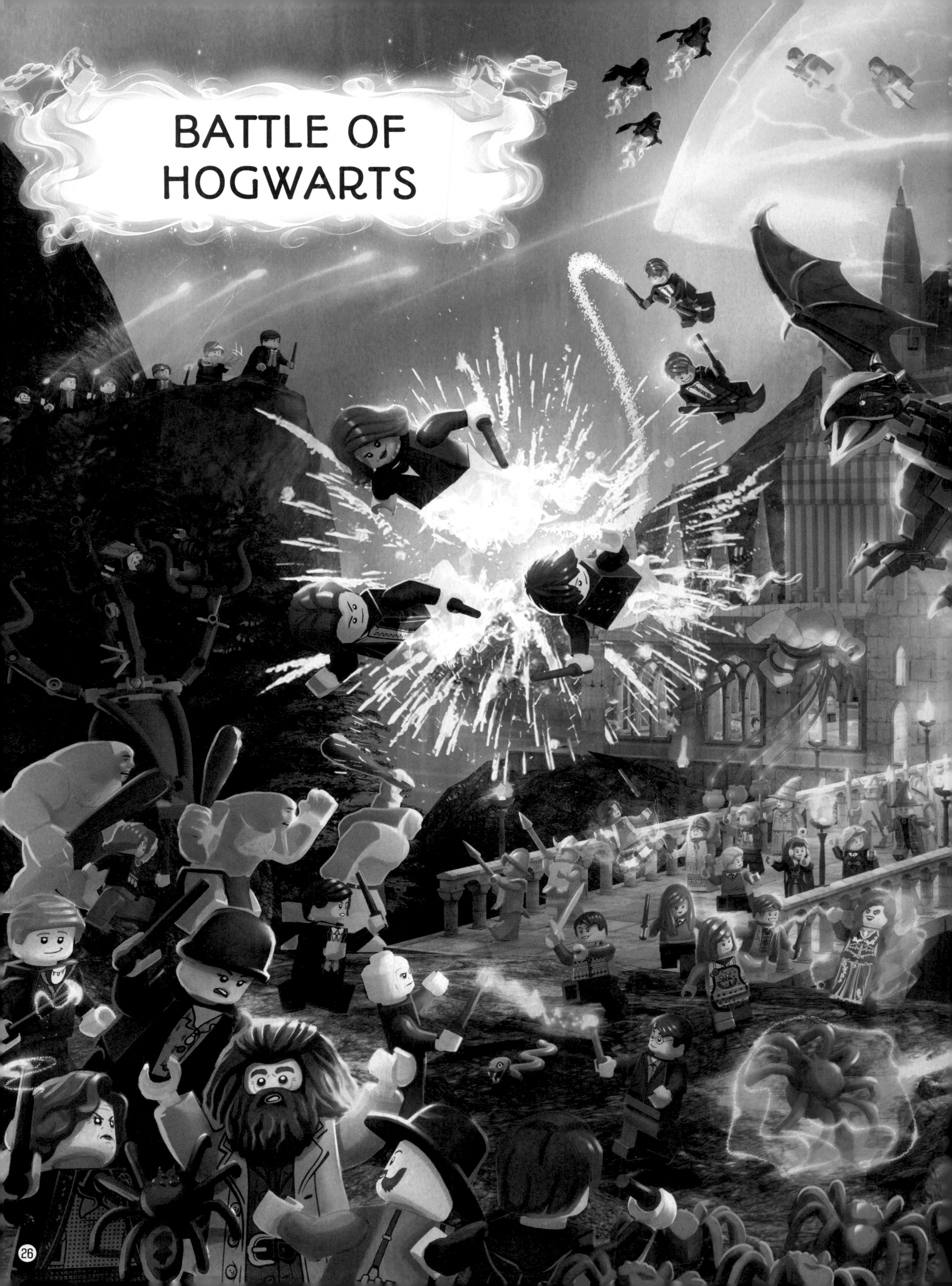

Hagrid

Prof. Sprout

Prof. Lupin

Voldemort

Dean

Prof. McGonagall

Nearly Headless Nick

Bellatrix Lestrange

Ginny

Neville

If you've come this far, it means you're at the end of the book. But there's a surprise task for you! You've found everybody on each page, but can you handle spotting more things? Take the challenge and go for it!

DIAGON ALLEY

1. Two tea boxes
2. Scroll
3. Cat
4. "Mad-Eye" Moody
5. Prof. Slughorn
6. Prof. Dumbledore
7. Hagrid
8. Goblin with coins
9. Wizard with top hat
10. Prof. Quirrell

THE GREAT HALL

1. Pixie
2. Rat
3. Spider
4. Malfoy
5. Lucian Bole
6. Prof. Trelawney
7. Nearly Headless Nick
8. Owl
9. Oliver
10. Prof. McGonagall

MOVING STAIRCASES

1. Basilisk
2. Three Mandrakes
3. Prof. Flitwick
4. Ghost
5. Prof. Dumbledore
6. Owl
7. Harry
8. Flint
9. Mme. Hooch
10. Filch

CORNISH PIXIES

1. Drawing
2. Portrait
3. Two brooms
4. Cage
5. Cat
6. Pixie with moustache
7. Dobby
8. Nearly Headless Nick
9. Malfoy
10. Seamus

PLATFORM 9¾

1. Owl
2. Mandrake
3. Hippogriff
4. Nearly Headless Nick
5. Mme. Hooch
6. Lucius Malfoy
7. Cho
8. Four Dementors
9. Hagrid
10. Prof. Trelawney

QUIDDITCH

1. Book
2. Guitar
3. Fred
4. Narcissa Malfoy
5. Dementor with bat
6. Hermione
7. Prof. Sprout
8. Prof. Lupin
9. Hagrid
10. Oliver

FIREWORKS

1. Lucius Malfoy
2. Dementor
3. Two Mandrakes
4. Ghost
5. Harry
6. Nearly Headless Nick
7. Prof. Umbridge
8. Fred
9. Owl
10. Filch

MINISTRY OF MAGIC

1. Dobby
2. Ollivander
3. Voldemort
4. Bellatrix Lestrange
5. Prof. Slughorn
6. Harry
7. Prof. McGonagall
8. Wizard with newspaper
9. Mermaid
10. George

WEASLEYS' WIZARD WHEEZES

1. Headless Hat
2. Quick-Quotes Quill
3. Five Fanged Frisbees
4. Mme. Hooch
5. Arthur Weasley
6. Ollivander
7. Narcissa Malfoy
8. Dementor with box
9. Hagrid
10. Prof. Dumbledore

GRINGOTTS WIZARDING BANK

1. Owl
2. Malfoy
3. Owl
4. Kingsley Shacklebolt
5. Prof. Slughorn
6. Mme. Hooch
7. Prof. Trelawney
8. Two Bellatrixes
9. Prof. Umbridge
10. Ghost

BATTLE OF HOGWARTS

1. Ron
2. Nagini
3. Prof. Flitwick
4. Cho
5. Luna
6. Mme. Hooch
7. Harry
8. Prof. Slughorn
9. Tonks
10. Ford Anglia

ANSWERS

DIAGON ALLEY

THE GREAT HALL

MOVING STAIRCASES

CORNISH PIXIES

PLATFORM 9¾

QUIDDITCH